D1643663

JASPER'S
STORY
Living with Cystic Fibrosis

Created by
Nandita Jain and Andy Glynne

W
FRANKLIN WATTS
LONDON • SYDNEY

Franklin Watts
First published in Great Britain in 2017 by The Watts Publishing Group

Mosaic Films, Shacklewell Lane, London E8 2EZ

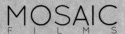

Created by Nandita Jain and Andy Glynne

Editor: Sarah Silver

ISBN 978 1 4451 5604 0

Printed in China

Franklin Watts
An imprint of
Hachette Children's Group
Part of The Watts Publishing Group
Carmelite House
50 Victoria Embankment
London EC4Y 0DZ

An Hachette UK Company
www.hachette.co.uk
www.franklinwatts.co.uk

My name is Jasper and I have cystic fibrosis.

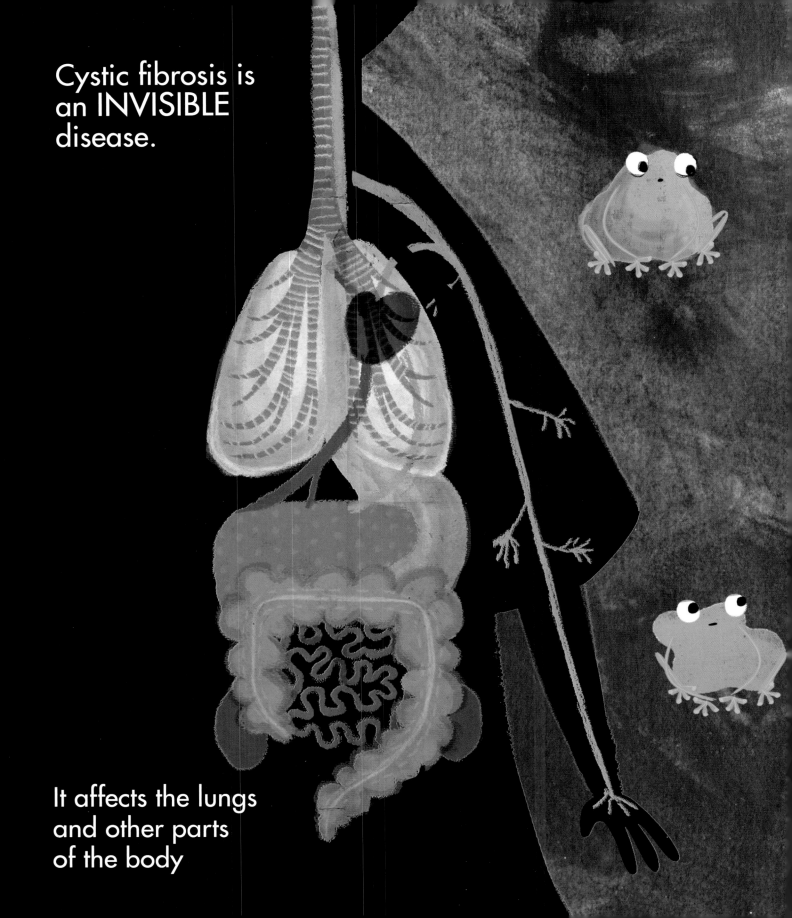

Cystic fibrosis is an INVISIBLE disease.

It affects the lungs and other parts of the body

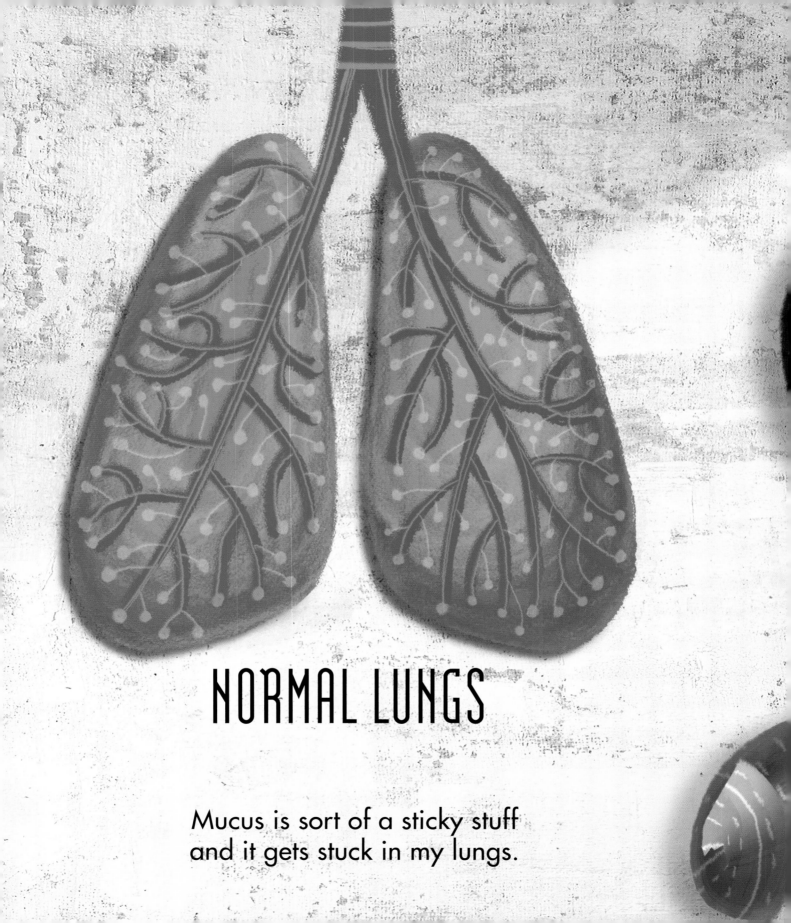

NORMAL LUNGS

Mucus is sort of a sticky stuff
and it gets stuck in my lungs.

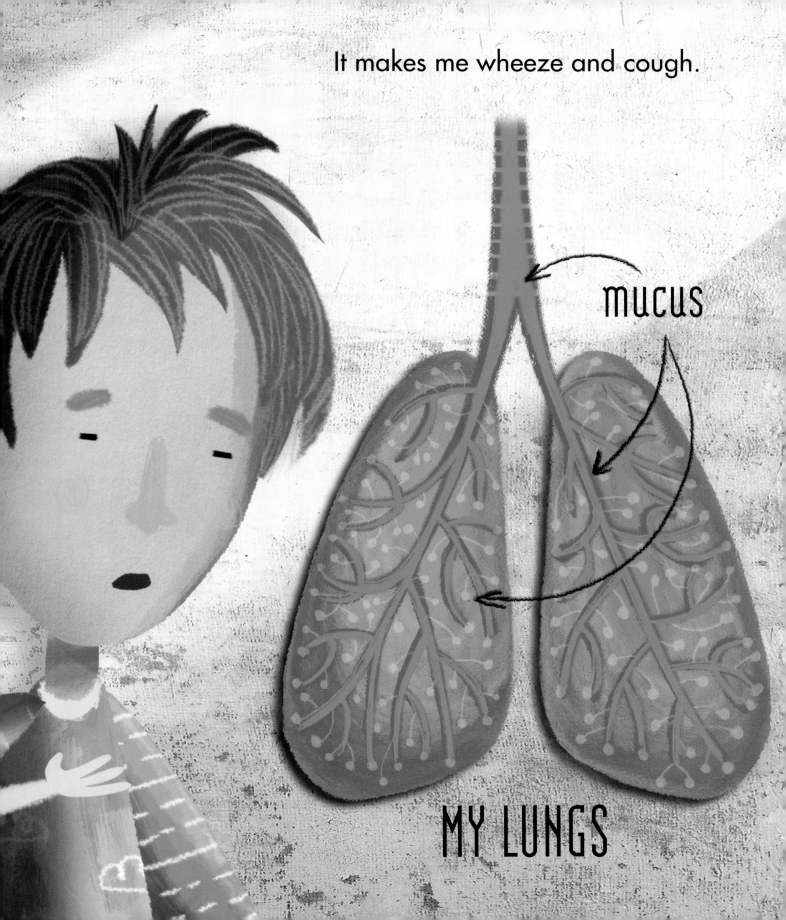

I cough the mucus out into a tissue.
Then my mum and dad have to check
what colour it is.

If it's PALE it's fine,
but if it's dark GREEN
then it's bad.

I have to wake up half an hour earlier than everyone else to start getting rid of the frogs.

I get up and I do my NEBULISER.

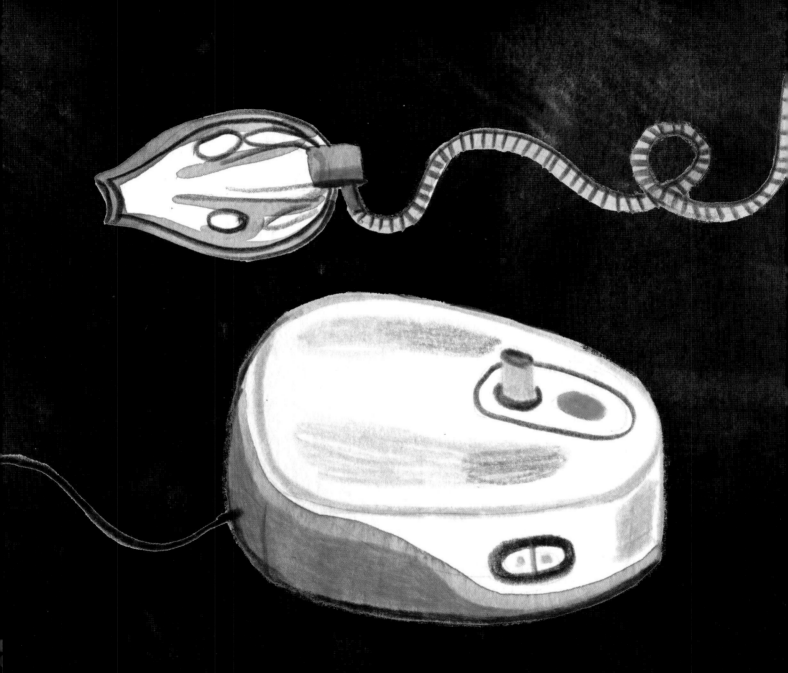

It's a big box that puffs out steam.

The nebuliser has a MOUTHPIECE and a PIPE.

I breathe in and the steam TICKLES the frogs ...

... and makes me
COUGH them out.

Then I have to go to school and
I do my ACAPELLA in the car. It's like
a thermometer that I breathe into.

It makes vibrations in my chest
and helps me to cough up more FROGS.

At school, I have to take tablets
and everyone stares at me.

All the kids ask, 'What's that?'
And I say, 'They're tablets.'

No one else at school is allowed to have chocolate.

But I need to eat chocolate because my body doesn't ABSORB fat as much as it should.

So I have to eat much MORE fatty food
than everyone else.

Sometimes my friends ask me if I want to come for a sleepover.

But I have to say
NO.

I tell them
it's because
I have to take all
my MEDICATION.

If I have dark green frogs,
I have to go to
HOSPITAL.

I get a PIPE up
my arm. It pumps
medicine into me.

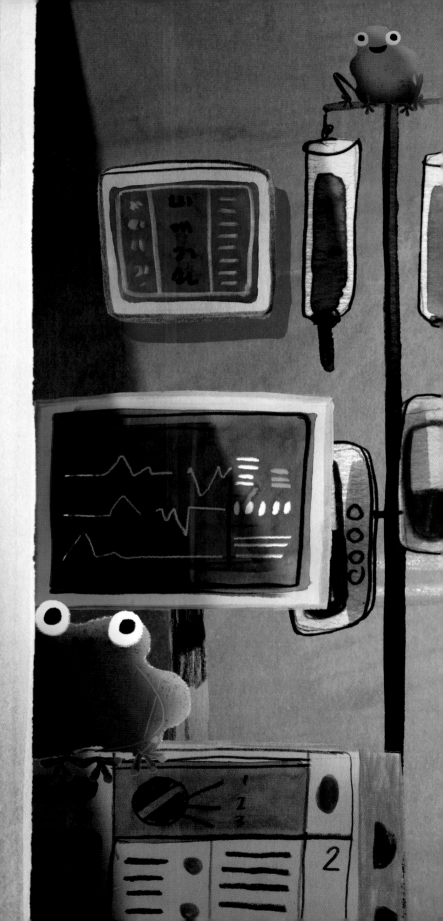

And when I've finished
that for a week,
I'm allowed to go HOME.

But then I still have to come back
to the hospital every night for
more medicine, until there are
NO MORE dark green frogs.

It's really
BORING
    at the hospital.

But the NURSES are
NICE and they
take good care of me.

I try to do lots of exercise because it gives me more energy.

The doctors say EXERCISE is really important.

Even bouncing on a TRAMPOLINE is good!

It moves the mucus around and makes it easier for the **FROGS** to come out.

I like PLAYING with my brother.
We like to play Lego, and football
in the garden. Sometimes we just
lie on my bed and watch TV.

But I don't get much time to play with my brother, because I have to do my **NEBULISER** several times a day.

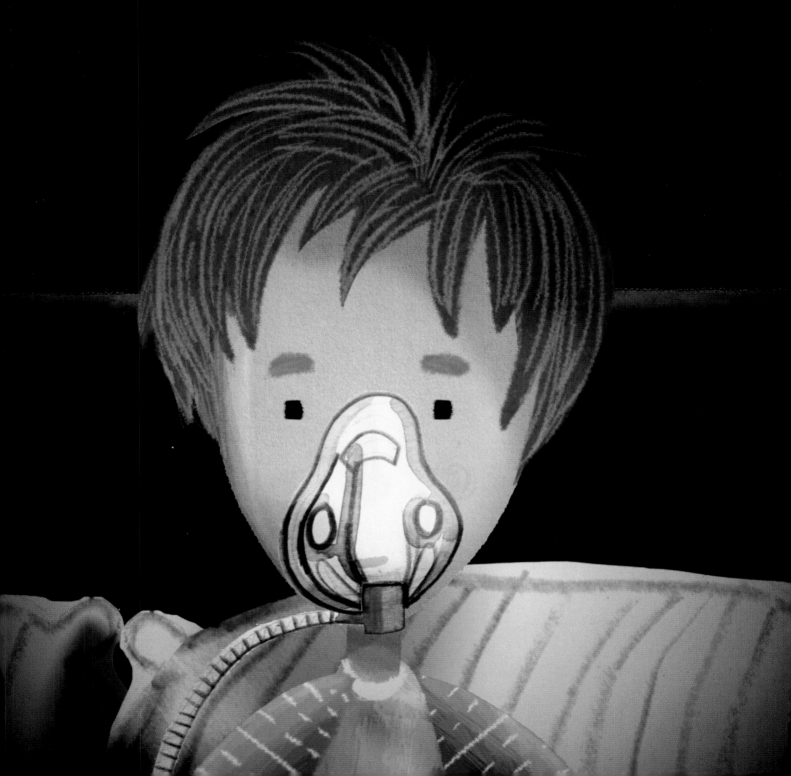

When everyone ELSE has frogs and they cough them out, that's the END of their frogs ...

... but I have **NEVER-ENDING** frogs.

FURTHER INFORMATION ABOUT CYSTIC FIBROSIS

Cystic fibrosis is a condition that you are born with. You cannot catch it from other people or develop it later in life, as happens with an illness such as heart disease. People with cystic fibrosis have the illness because a faulty gene was passed to them by each of their parents.

What is a gene?

A gene is an instruction that tells a bit of the body how to work. In the case of cystic fibrosis, the gene affects how salt and water move in and out of every cell in the body – and not in a good way. This causes thick, sticky mucus, called 'frogs' in this book, to build up inside the lungs and other parts of the body.

An invisible illness

Because cystic fibrosis affects part of the body on the inside, it is often called an invisible illness. People might look quite healthy at first glance. However, the thick mucus makes people wheeze or cough, makes it difficult for them to digest food and can lead to weak bones and other health issues. Having cystic fibrosis also makes it hard to breathe – some people say climbing the stairs feels like climbing a mountain. However, the condition affects each person differently.

What can be done?

Although there is no cure, there are many treatments. Children with the condition are taught how to clear their lungs of mucus by coughing it up. Medicines taken as pills help people to digest food more easily. Exercise can help clear the mucus and make the person more healthy so that they don't catch as many coughs and colds. Taking advice on what to eat can also help. In addition, scientists are working across the world to find out more about the condition and how to improve treatments in the future.

For more information and resources, visit www.cysticfibrosis.org.uk/body.
For support and information, contact the Cystic Fibrosis Trust helpline on 0300 373 1000 or email helpline@cysticfibrosis.org.uk.

Cystic Fibrosis Trust

The complete Living with... series.
Real-life testimonies of children living with illness.

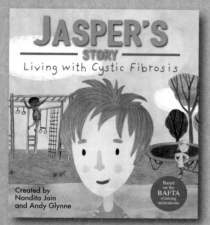

JASPER'S STORY
Living with Cystic Fibrosis
Created by Nandita Jain and Andy Glynne
Based on the BAFTA winning animations

978 14451 5604 0

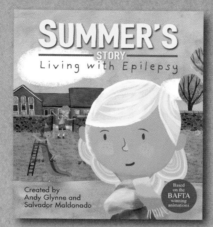

SUMMER'S STORY
Living with Epilepsy
Created by Andy Glynne and Salvador Maldonado
Based on the BAFTA winning animations

978 14451 5666 8

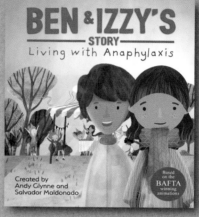

BEN & IZZY'S STORY
Living with Anaphylaxis
Created by Andy Glynne and Salvador Maldonado
Based on the BAFTA winning animations

978 14451 5662 0

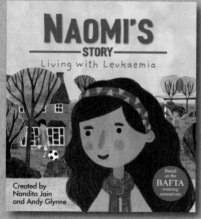

NAOMI'S STORY
Living with Leukaemia
Created by Nandita Jain and Andy Glynne
Based on the BAFTA winning animations

978 14451 5668 2

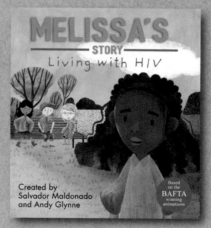

MELISSA'S STORY
Living with HIV
Created by Salvador Maldonado and Andy Glynne
Based on the BAFTA winning animations

978 14451 5664 4

W
FRANKLIN WATTS

www.franklinwatts.co.uk